GRADE 1
MEASUREMENT
Fun-filled Activities

Om
KIDZ
An imprint of Om Books International

Hundreds Chart Challenge

Length is how long or tall something is from end to end. Length also shows how far something is from a certain point. We use the words **long, short, tall** to show length.

Tools to measure length

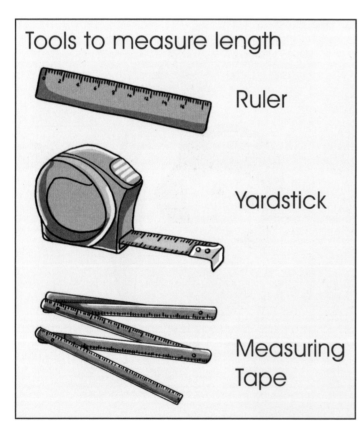

Ruler

Yardstick

Measuring Tape

Units to measure length

Inch

Foot

Centimetre

Metre

Kilometre

When you hear "centimetre"... think about...

When you hear "inch"... think about...

Longer Than and Shorter Than

Write the words longer than or shorter than to make the sentences true.

Abby is _____ Spot.

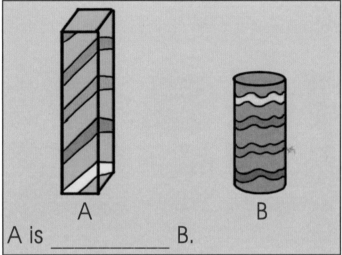

A is _____ B.

The American Flag hat is _____ the chef's hat.

The lighter bat's wing span is _____ the darker bat's wing span.

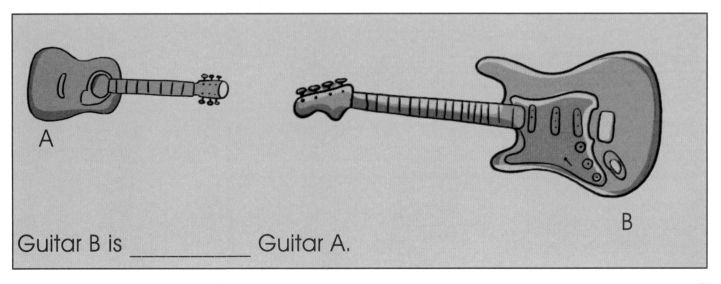

Guitar B is _____ Guitar A.

Measuring Length

There are standard as well as non-standard units of measuring length. Standard units give us accurate measurement so we prefer standard units over non-standard units of measurement.

Non-standard units

blocks   book   pencils

legos   eraser   counting cubes

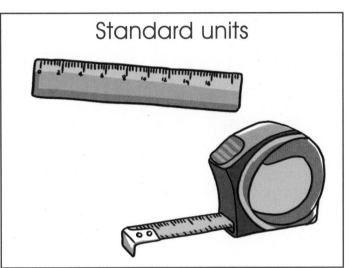

Standard units

Measure each object using blocks and write the number.

☐ blocks

☐ blocks

☐ blocks

☐ blocks

☐ blocks

☐ blocks

Measuring Length Using Standard Units

We use a ruler and metre tape to measure length in centimetres and inches.

Steps and rules for measuring length:

1. Line up the beginning of the object with the beginning of the measuring tool.

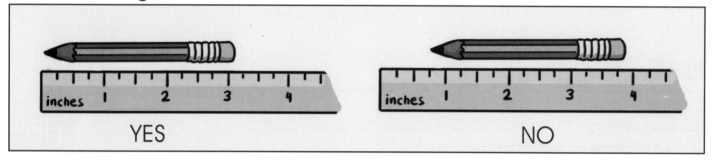

2. Put the unit marks close to the object you are measuring.

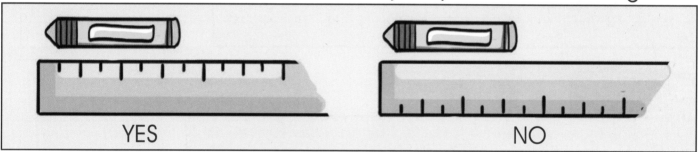

3. Make sure the measuring tool doesn't slip.

4. Don't overlap or stack the tool.

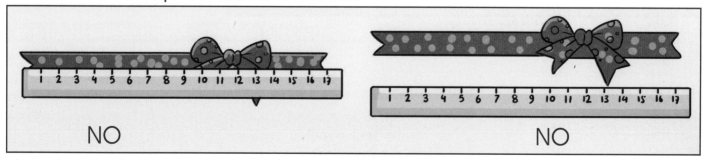

Just Measuring By

Let us measure length using centimetres. Here is an example:

This ribbon is
4 centimetres long.

Write how many centimetres each picture measures.

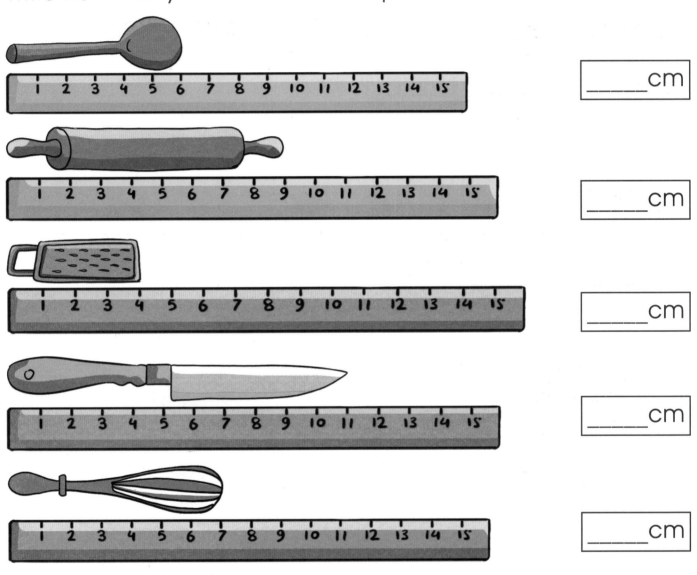

_____cm

_____cm

_____cm

_____cm

_____cm

NICE IDEA!

Draw a large circle and put eyes inside, leave a place to glue the smile. What is the length of the smile in centimetres?

Get, Set, Go!

Use a ruler and measure each line in centimetres. Write on the blanks.

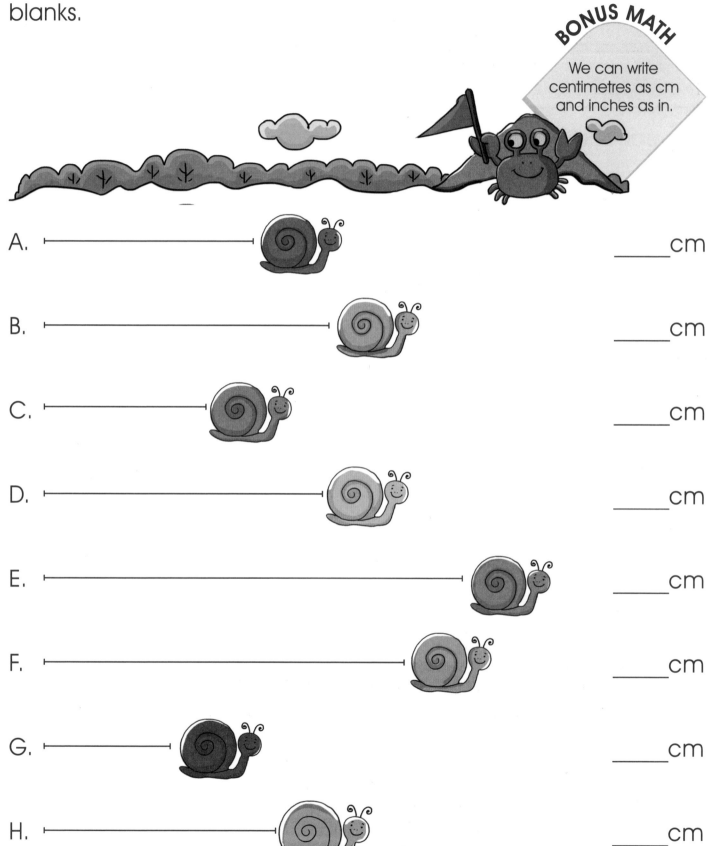

A. _____ cm

B. _____ cm

C. _____ cm

D. _____ cm

E. _____ cm

F. _____ cm

G. _____ cm

H. _____ cm

Inch By Inch

We measure length in inches too.

The ear bud is **3 inches** long.

BONUS MATH
We use bigger units like metres and kilometres to measure long distances.

Write how many inches each picture measures.

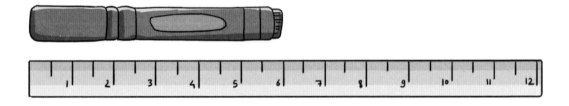

_____ in

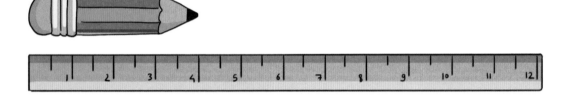

_____ in

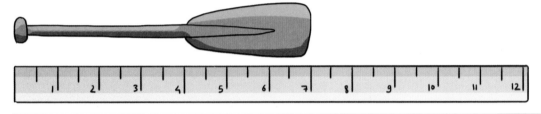

_____ in

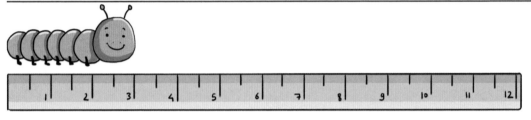

_____ in

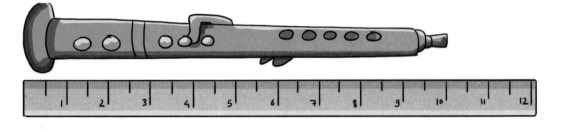

_____ in

Measure It!

Find a friend and write down the measurements stated below. Use a measuring tape and write the measurement in inches.

How tall?

_____ inches

Length of arm

_____ inches

Length of a leg

_____ inches

Length of foot

_____ inches

Length of hand span

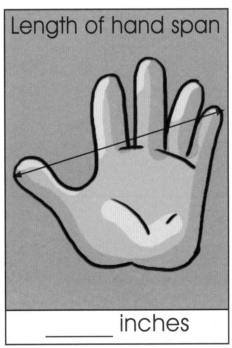

_____ inches

Around the head

_____ inches

NICE IDEA!

Measure your hand along side your friend's in inches. Whose hand is longer and by how many inches?

Weight

When we measure the weight of something, we find out how **heavy** it is. We use the words heavy and **light** to show weight.

The cat is **heavier than** the mouse.
It is hard to tell the weight of objects by holding them so we use different tools and units to measure weight.

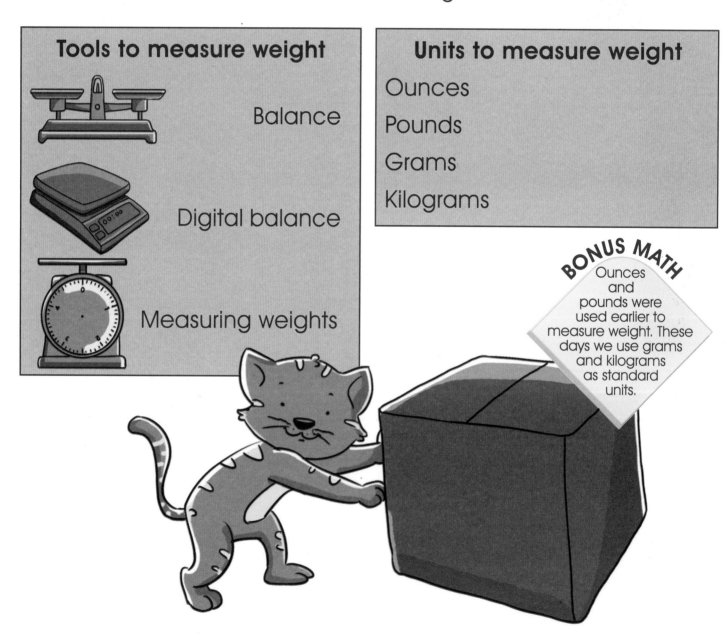

Tools to measure weight	Units to measure weight
Balance	Ounces
Digital balance	Pounds
Measuring weights	Grams
	Kilograms

BONUS MATH
Ounces and pounds were used earlier to measure weight. These days we use grams and kilograms as standard units.

A Heavy Load to Haul

Mr. Mouse is ready to head down the road with a heavy load. Write **H** in the boxes to help him decide which things to carry on the truck.

A Balancing Act!

Compare each item in the chart with
a small box of crayons.
Draw a tick (✓) in the correct box.

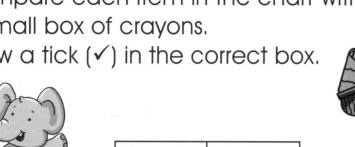

	Heavier than 🖍	Lighter than 🖍		Heavier than 🖍	Lighter than 🖍

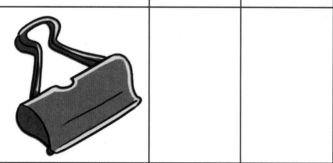					

NICE IDEA!

Draw and label something lighter than a
can of soup.

It's Like a See-saw

How does a balance work?

We place weights or units on one side of the balance and the object to be measured on the other side.

BONUS MATH
When a balance scale is levelled, the two sides have the same weight.

Write **H** for heavy and **L** for light to show heavy and light for each side of the balance. Write **E** if both the sides are equal.

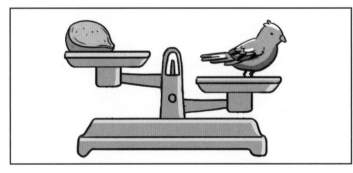

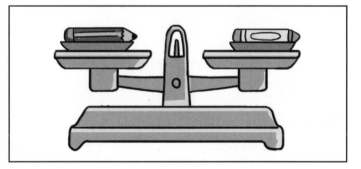

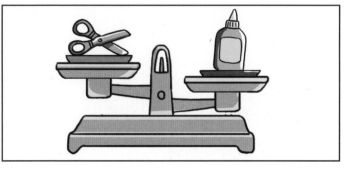

How Much Does Each Object Weigh?

Let us measure the weight of some objects using cubes.

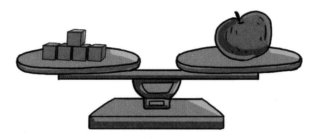

The weight of apple = 5 cubes

How much does each object weigh? Write the number of cubes.

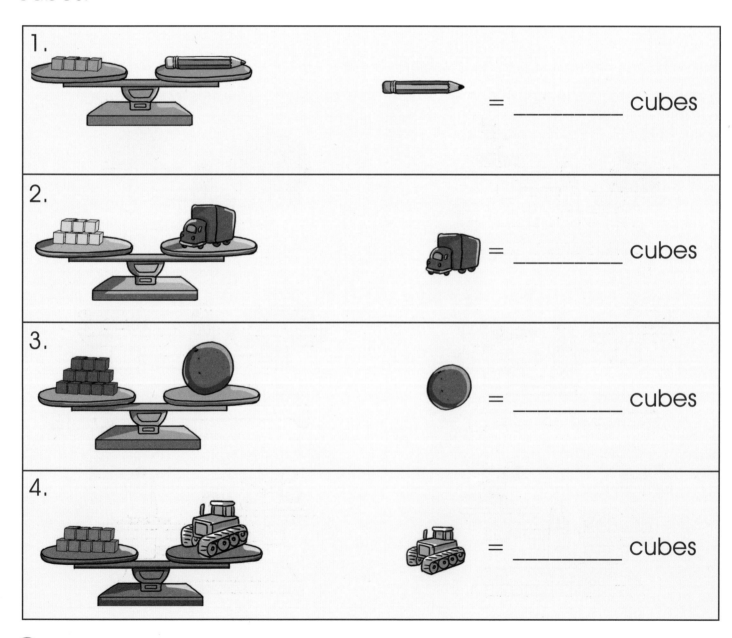

1.

_____ = _____ cubes

2.

_____ = _____ cubes

3.

_____ = _____ cubes

4.

_____ = _____ cubes

Measuring in Grams

We measure the weight of objects in grams and kilograms.

Let us see an example.

These are the masses we use to measure.

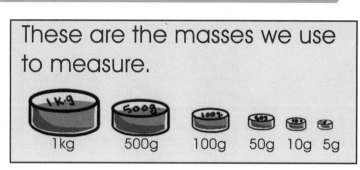

1kg   500g   100g   50g   10g   5g

The strawberry weighs 10 grams.

BONUS MATH

We also write grams as g and kilograms as kg.

How much does each object weigh?

The teddy bear weighs _____.

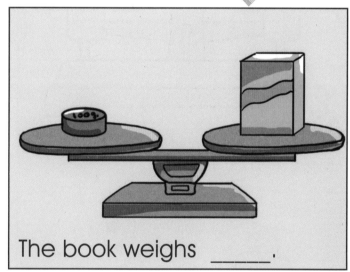

The book weighs _____.

The fish tank weighs _____.

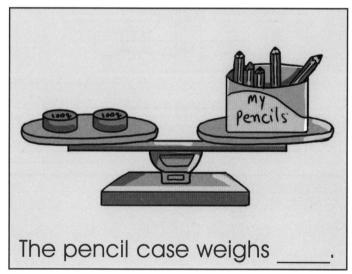

The pencil case weighs _____.

Measuring in Kilograms

We can also measure objects in kilograms.

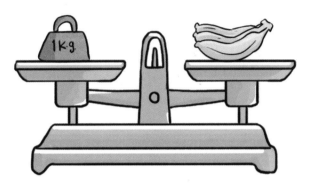

These bananas weigh 1 kilogram.

How much does each object weigh?

The oranges weigh _____

The bag weighs _____

The puppy weighs _____

The box weighs _____

NICE IDEA!

Visit a green grocer or fruitseller. What kind of weighing scales does he have? Observe. Draw them.

Measure It!

You need:

crayons
glue
paper clip
cap
lunch box
stapler
water bottle
toy

Do:

- Pick two items.
- Put one on each side of the balance and measure.
- Write which one is heavier.

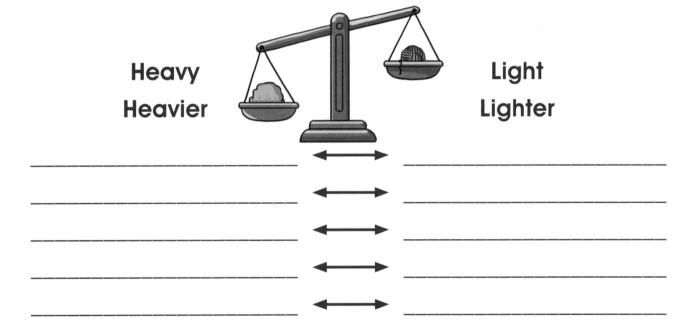

Heavy
Heavier

Light
Lighter

_____		_____
_____		_____
_____		_____
_____		_____
_____		_____

NICE IDEA!

What more to discover?

- Measure each of the given objects using weights.
- Make your own chart with names of objects and their weight in grams and kilograms.

Capacity

Capacity is how much a container can hold.

The jug **holds more** water than the cup.

It is hard to tell the capacity of objects just by filling containers so we use different tools and units to measure weight. For example:

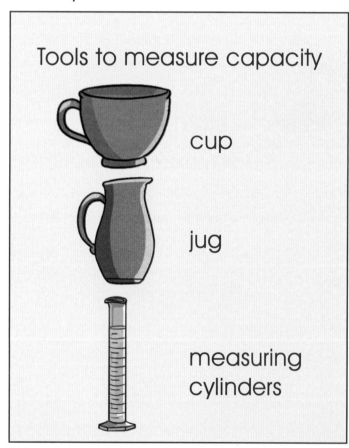

Tools to measure capacity

cup

jug

measuring cylinders

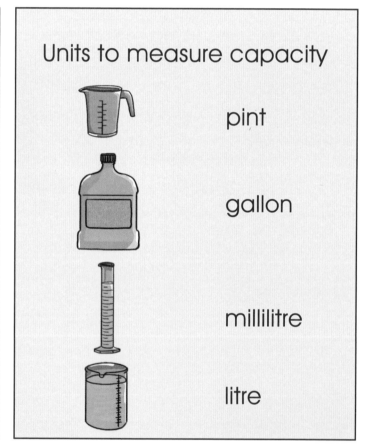

Units to measure capacity

pint

gallon

millilitre

litre

NICE IDEA!

Mr. Franklin filled a bucket with water to clean his floor. Does his bucket hold 9 litres or 9 millilitres of water?

Sweet is the Treat!

Look at each pair of containers in Jumbo's Store.
Circle the container that holds more.

Arrange the containers in the order of increasing capacity.
Number the containers 1, 2, 3, 4 and 5.

NICE IDEA!

How can we know without measuring which container holds more and which less? Discuss.

How Much Does it Hold?

1 gallon holds more than 1 litre

1 litre

1 cup holds less than 1 litre

Draw a circle around the things that **hold more** than **1 litre**.

Draw a square around the things that **hold less** than **1 litre**.

NICE IDEA!

Draw and label something that can hold more water than your bottle.

Measuring Capacity Rules

1. Count each cup you use as you fill your container.

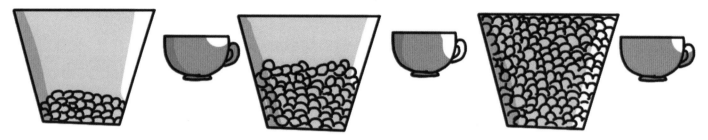

2. Fill your container to the top but don't overflow.

3. Make sure your cup is filled to the top every time.

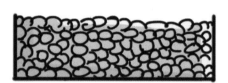   

NICE IDEA!

1. Collect 5 containers of different sizes from your kitchen.
2. Use the smallest container to measure the capacity of the other 4 containers.
3. Record your observations in the table.

Name of container	Number of smallest containers used to fill it

Plenty of Room

Choose the unit you would use to measure the liquid in each item.
Write ml for millilitre and L for litre.

Grade 1: Measurement

Measuring Capacity in Millilitres and Litres

Circle the closest measurement for each object. Write the measurement on the line.

____ML
400   4

____L
20   2

____ML
200   2

____L
1   10

____ML
50   500

____L
30   3

____L
40   4

____ML
1   100

____L
2   200

NICE IDEA!

How much do about 20 drops of water measure-a millilitre or litre? Find out without actual measurement. What's that secret way?

| morning | noon | evening | night |

Circle the things that happen before noon.

Circle the things that happen after noon.

NICE IDEA!

Draw a picture to show something that you do before noon.

Which takes more time? Tick the picture.

Which takes less time? Tick the picture.

Which animal would take the least time to reach the finish line?

Tick against it.

NICE IDEA!

Which takes more time – making a paper boat or drawing a boat?

Tick Tock, Meet The Clock!

A clock tells us the time. A clock has two hands. The small hand shows the hour. The long hand shows the minutes. When the **hour hand** points to a number and the **minute hand** points to **12**, we say the time as **o'clock.**

The **hour hand** points to 4. The time is 4 o'clock or 4:00.

minute hand

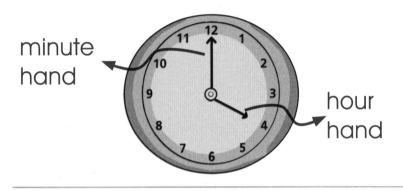

hour hand

BONUS MATH

Read the hour hand first and then the minute hand.

Read the time on the clock. Write it in both ways.

_____

_____

_____

_____

_____

_____

_____

_____

_____

_____

_____

_____

Grade 1: Measurement

Half Past the Hour

When the long hand points to 6, we say the time as **half past** the hour. When it's half past, the long hand is half way around the clock and the hour hand is half way between the hour numbers.

The hour hand is between 1 and 2. The minute hand is at 6. The time is half past 1 or 1:30.

BONUS MATH

We also say 1:30 as "one thirty".

Read the time on the clock. Write the time both the ways.

_____   _____   _____   _____

_____   _____   _____   _____

_____   _____   _____   _____

_____   _____   _____   _____

Write the Time

____ : ____   ____ : ____   ____ : ____   ____ : ____

____ : ____   ____ : ____   ____ : ____   ____ : ____

____ : ____   ____ : ____   ____ : ____   ____ : ____

THINK

Miss Teddy starts cleaning her house at 7:00. She cleans for 30 minutes. What time is it when she stops? _____ : _____.

Where are My Hands?

Draw hands on the clock to match the time written below each clock.

4:00

05:00

06:00

11:30

07:00

02:00

08:30

03:00

NICE IDEA!

Draw a clock to show what time it is right now.

Answer Key

Page 3

1. Abby is shorter than Spot.

2. A is longer than B.

3. The American Flag hat is shorter than the chef's hat.

4. The lighter bat's wing span is longer than the darker bat's wing span.

5. Guitar B is longer than Guitar A.

Page 4

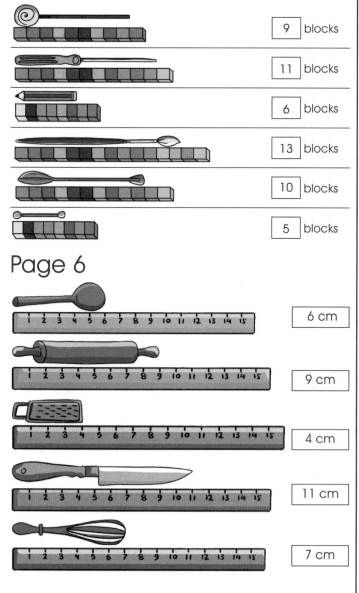

	9	blocks
11	blocks
6	blocks
13	blocks
10	blocks
5	blocks

Page 6

| 6 cm |
| 9 cm |
| 4 cm |
| 11 cm |
| 7 cm |

Page 7

Children will do on their own.

Page 8

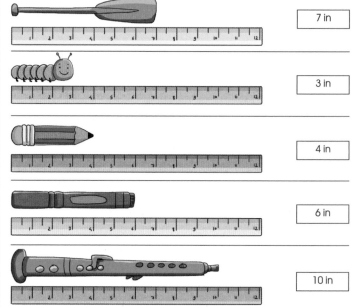

| 7 in |
| 3 in |
| 4 in |
| 6 in |
| 10 in |

Page 9

Children will do on their own. Answer will vary.

Page 11

Answer Key

Page 12

	Heavier than	Lighter than		Heavier than	Lighter than
	✓				✓
		✓			✓
		✓			✓

Page 13

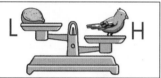
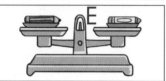

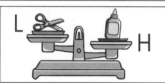

H ... L   H ... L
L ... H   E
H ... L   L ... H

Page 14

1. 4 cubes

2. 7 cubes

3. 12 cubes

4. 9 cubes

Page 15

The teddy bear weighs 300 g.

The book weighs 100 g.

The fish tank weighs 50 g.

The pencil case weighs 200g.

Page 16

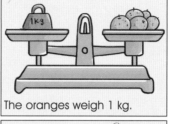

The oranges weigh 1 kg.

The bag weighs 2 kg.

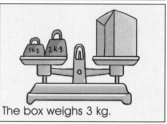

The puppy weighs 5 kg.

The box weighs 3 kg.

Page 17

Children will do on their own.

Page 19

4   1   3   2   5

Page 20

Answer Key

Page 22

ml	ml	L	ml
ml	L	L	ml
ml	L	ml	ml

Page 24

Page 25

Page 26

12 o'clock
12:00

3 o'clock
3:00

11 o'clock
11:00

8 o'clock
8:00

5 o'clock
5:00

10 o'clock
10:00

Page 27

half past 4
4:30

half past 6
6:30

half past 9
9:30

half past 5
5:30

half past 2
2:30

half past 10
10:30

half past 7
7:30

half past 4
4:30

Page 28

10:00

2:30

7:30

3:00

4:30

9:30

5:00

12:00

8:00

2:00

11:30

1:30

Page 29

Children will do on their own.

Grade 1: Measurement